Summer Solutions.
Minutes a Day–Mastery for a Lifetime!

Common Core
ENGLISH GRAMMAR
& Mechanics
5

Nancy L. McGraw
Nancy Tondy
Regina Webb

Joan Archer
Diane Dillon
Patricia Kecskemety

Bright Ideas Press, LLC
Cleveland, OH

Summer Solutions
Common Core
English Grammar & Mechanics 5

Printed in the United States of America

The writers of *Summer Solutions* Common Core English Grammar & Mechanics aligned the series in accordance with information from the following:

National Governors Association Center for Best Practices,
Council of Chief State School Officers.
Common Core State Standards, English Language Arts.
National Governors Association Center for Best Practices,
Council of Chief State School Officers, Washington, D.C., 2010.

ISBN: 978-1-60873-062-9

Cover Design: Dan Mazzola
Editor: Christopher Backs

Instructions for Parents / Guardians

- *Summer Solutions* is an extension of the *Simple Solutions* Approach being used by thousands of children in schools across the United States.

- This summer book aligns with the English Language Arts Common Core State Standards, which identify key ideas, understandings, and skills appropriate for this particular grade level. The Common Core State Standards addressed in this book are listed on the next page.

- The 30 lessons included in each workbook are meant to review and reinforce the skills learned in the grade level just completed.

- The program is designed to be used three days per week for ten weeks to ensure retention. Completing the book all at one time defeats the purpose of sustained practice over the summer break.

- The answers for each lesson are found in the back of the book. Lessons should be checked immediately after completion for optimal feedback. Items that were difficult for students or done incorrectly should be resolved right away to ensure mastery.

- Help Pages (also toward the back of the book) list the parts of speech, punctuation and capitalization rules, and other information meant to help students complete the lessons independently.

- Adjust the use of the book to fit vacations. More lessons may have to be completed during the weeks before or following a family vacation.

Summer Solutions
Common Core
English Grammar & Mechanics 5

Reviewed Skills Include   Standard

Help Pages begin on page 63.

Answers to Lessons begin on page 77.

Lesson #1

1. Read the sentences below. Draw a line through the fragment and rewrite it as a complete sentence on the line.

   Marla and Cheryl wanted to ride to the park, but one of their bikes had a flat tire. Only low on air. Cheryl quickly pumped it up, and they went on their way.

   _____

2. Choose a word to complete each sentence.

   command   simple   conjunction   compound

   A _____ sentence has one complete thought.

   A _____ sentence has more than one complete thought.

3. Underline the part that states an *effect*.

   The plant leaves began to droop since
   Travis had forgotten to water them again.

4. The verbs in this sentence do not agree. Keep the verbs in past tense. Cross out the incorrect verb and write it correctly on the line.

   Shayla crouched low on her skis and crosses

   the finish line for her first victory of the season.

   _____

5. What is the meaning of the underlined word?

   Matteo was always late for school. His <u>implausible</u> explanations for his tardiness fooled no one.

   believable   far-fetched   tedious

6. Correctly punctuate the title of the book in this sentence.

   I loved The Sixty-Eight Rooms, a book about miniature sixth graders.

7. **A relative pronoun introduces a part of a sentence that relates to an antecedent.**

   Example: The person <u>whose</u> wallet I found was very grateful.

                ↑   ↑

       antecedent   relative pronoun

   Underline the relative pronoun; circle its antecedent.

   The movie that I watched last night had several surprising plot twists.

8. Insert commas.

   Every morning I brush my teeth pack my backpack and eat a big breakfast.

9. Choose the correct word to complete each sentence.

   A salamander is an amphibian that spends part of (it's / its) life cycle on land and part in water.

   Salamanders are usually under rocks and logs, so (it's / its) unusual to spot a salamander unless you're looking for one.

10. Circle the words that should be capitalized.

   saturday   thanksgiving day   january   spring

   birthday   my grandfather   aunt edith   ms. martin

Lesson #2

1. Match each sentence with the way *can* is used.

    A) is able to   B) has permission to

    _____ Shannon <u>can</u> use the phone in the office.

    _____ Do you think this zipper <u>can</u> be fixed?

2. Complete the sentence using the <u>present perfect tense</u> of *write*.

    Megan _____ the final copy of her book report.

3. Read each phrase. Label the verb action or being.

    is late _____   can be _____

    may go _____   will run _____

4. **Correlative conjunctions always work in pairs within a sentence.**

    Example: The hurricane **not only** flooded the streets **but also** damaged buildings.

    Insert the correlative conjunction pair that best completes the sentence. A list of conjunction pairs can be found in the *Help Pages*.

    Since we must choose, we _____ can make

    pancakes _____ scrambled

    eggs for our campfire breakfast.

5. Use proofreader's symbols to correct the capitalization errors in this sentence. See the *Help Pages* for proofreader's symbols.

    jordan is a Lifeguard this Summer at fell

    lake in northfield, Ohio.

6. Keep the verbs in present tense. Cross out the incorrect verb and write it correctly on the line.

    Mandy saves her allowance and spent it
    on a scarf for her mother.   _____

7. Identify each underlined word. Choose *adverb* or *preposition*.

    There is space in the luggage rack
    <u>above</u> your seat.

        adverb   preposition

    We watched as the trapeze artist
    performed high <u>above</u>.

        adverb   preposition

8. Insert a comma after introductory word(s).

    Well this will be the last time we can bowl here.

    Hooray you were the top scorer this round!

9. Underline the complete predicate and double underline the simple predicate.

    The fluffy white dog scratched at the back door.

10. Make these nouns plural.

    ox _____   child _____

    mouse _____   knife _____

Lesson #3

1. Use commas to separate items in a series.

   Tanya bakes four kinds of cookies for the PTA bake sale: chocolate chip oatmeal peanut butter and sugar.

2. Correlative conjunctions always work in pairs within a sentence. Fill in the second half of the correlative conjunction pair.

   Neither Caroline _____ her brother Theo have been assigned to a team.

3. **Future tense uses a helping verb (*will* or *shall*).** Use the verb *dress* to correctly complete this sentence in the future tense.

   Wyatt _____ as the backup goalie for the hockey game.

4. Correctly punctuate the following sentences with commas.

   Isabella did you remember to bring a beach towel?

   I was certain it was a tie weren't you?

   No thank you.

5. Correctly punctuate the name of the magazine in this sentence.

   Harper wrote a poem that was published in the spring issue of Creative Kids.

6. What is the meaning of the underlined word?

   As it cooled, the Jell-O began to <u>congeal</u>.

   spill over   change color   thicken   melt

7. Sort these nouns.

> Latinos   uncle   tourist   summer
> Chicago   Pizza Hut   automobile   Ford Explorer

proper: _____

common: _____

8. Match these Greek and Latin roots with their meanings. Use the definitions in the *Help Pages*.

_____ light   A) gram

_____ writing   B) phon

_____ fear   C) morph

_____ sound   D) photo

_____ shape   E) phobe

Arachibutyrophobia
Fear of peanut butter sticking to the roof of the mouth.

9. **A metaphor compares two things by saying one thing *is* another.**

The new chef is a wizard in the kitchen.

What two things are being compared in the metaphor?

_____   _____

What does the metaphor mean?

A) The new chef uses magic.
B) The new chef is an excellent cook.
C) The new chef is a wizard.

10. Write the irregular plurals for these nouns.

> louse   child   person   tooth

_____ _____ _____ _____

Lesson #4

1. Underline the part of the sentence that states the <u>cause</u> and double underline the part of the sentence that states the <u>effect</u>.

   Lila was invited to Ohio's anti-smoking conference because her poster won first place in the county-wide competition.

2. Read the sentence. Are the underlined words synonyms or antonyms?

   Every Sunday, Zoe liked to <u>peruse</u> the newspaper for hours, but Remy preferred to <u>glance</u> at the headlines.

          synonyms   antonyms

   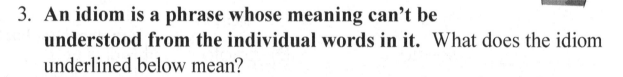

3. **An idiom is a phrase whose meaning can't be understood from the individual words in it.** What does the idiom underlined below mean?

   If I could find the person who broke this vase, I would give him a <u>piece of my mind</u>.

   A) trade places with him   C) have him clean it up

   B) scold him   D) none of these

4. **A main verb that ends in** *–ing* **with a helping verb forms the progressive tense.** Use the <u>present progressive form</u> of the verb *practice* to complete the sentence.

   Amanda _____ _____ for her recital.

5. Correctly punctuate the following sentence.

   The orchestra is playing well tonight don't you think?

6. Place a comma in the compound sentence. Circle the coordinating conjunction.

   Everyone likes Amanda's new bike but a few of us are too small to ride it.

7. Choose the verb tense that correctly completes each sentence.

   We learned about the greenhouse effect and (write / wrote) about its impact.

   Eleanor mails the letters and (shovels / shoveled) the sidewalk.

8. Find the word *taciturn* in a thesaurus or dictionary. Underline the meaning of *taciturn*.

   | well-behaved | chatty |
   | reluctant to talk | high temperature |

9. Complete the sentence by writing the <u>future perfect tense</u> of *fill*.

   Fernando _____ seventeen piñatas for the festival.

10. Add a comma and quotation marks to the sentence below.

    Malika inquired Is this the 1500-meter race or the mile run?

Lesson #5

1. **A subject pronoun replaces a noun as the subject of a sentence.** Find a list of subjective case pronouns in the *Help Pages*. Replace each underlined subject with a subject pronoun.

   <u>Lu and Jax</u> are learning to snowboard this winter. _____

   <u>Grace and I</u> are going to ski at Holiday Valley. _____

2. Underline the relative pronoun; circle its antecedent.

   The child whose mittens we found is looking in the lost and found now.

3. Choose a coordinating conjunction to complete each compound sentence.

   nor   so   but

   Ella was on time for school, _____ her sister was ten minutes late.

   Milo barked at Ivy's cat, _____ we brought the dog inside.

4. Underline the complete subject and double underline the simple subject.

   The powerful cougar buries some of its prey to eat later.

5. Label each sentence and add the proper end punctuation.

   _____ It looks like it might snow__   A) exclamatory

   _____ Do you know how many inches are expected__   B) declarative

   _____ Put your boots on__   C) imperative

   _____ Oh my goodness, it's snowing already__   D) interrogative

6. Use context clues to determine the meaning of the underlined word.

The cassette tapes that were popular in the twentieth century are <u>obsolete</u> now that there are CDs and MP3s.

modern   confusing   desirable   outdated

7. Match each word to a part of the *i before e except after c or when sounding like /ā/* spelling rule.

_____ neighbor   A) i before e

_____ friend   B) except after c

_____ conceit   C) or when sounding like /ā/

8. **A simile compares two things using the words *like* or *as*.**

Mr. McCann's fingers were as cold as ice.

What two things are being compared?

_____   _____

What does the simile mean?

A) His fingers were made of ice.
B) The bus was made of cold metal.
C) His fingers were very, very cold.
D) The bus was overdue.

9. Fill in the <u>present progressive tense form</u> of the verb *finish*.

Dylan _____ the last book in the series.

10. Underline the relative adverb. Double underline its antecedent.

The time when the team needs to board the bus is noon.

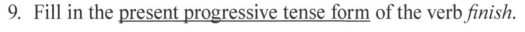

Lesson #6

1. **An object pronoun is in the predicate because it receives the action of the verb.** Find a list of objective case pronouns in the *Help Pages*. Replace each underlined noun with an object pronoun.

   Owen caught the ball and tossed it to <u>Eli</u>.   _____

   Micah put <u>his spikes</u> on and ran onto the field.   _____

   Roberta invited <u>Kim and I</u> to watch the game.   _____

2. Read the sentences. Are the underlined words synonyms or antonyms?   _____

   Mr. Henry told me this topic is <u>irrelevant</u> and should be deleted. He told me that another topic is <u>pertinent</u>, and I should write more about it.

3. Insert a comma wherever it is needed in the sentence.

   I think it is warm enough to go swimming today don't you agree?

4. There are errors in the writing below. Draw a line through the fragment. Circle two other errors.

   One of the best books i ever read was about a boy who run away from home. He survived in the wilderness for several weeks. No camping gear, food, or cell phone.

5. Write the seven coordinating conjunctions.

   _____

6. Underline the complete predicate and double underline the simple predicate.

Henry will have received his diploma by now.

Dad was considering taking us to the amusement park.

7. Use a pair of correlative conjunctions to complete the sentence.

To earn some money, _____ do yard work _____ baby-sit.

8. The root –*ology* means "study of." Match each word with its clue.

_____ study of animals   A) geology

_____ study of hearing   B) zoology

_____ study of Earth   C) audiology

9. Underline the idiom in this sentence. What does the idiom mean?

Winning the Pinewood Derby was great, but meeting the president of the United States was the icing on the cake.

A) cake frosting   C) lots of fun

B) the best part of a good thing   D) a celebration

10. Correctly punctuate the title of the website in this sentence.

Jennifer researched soccer rules on the www.usyouthsoccer.org website.

Lesson #7

1. Use a possessive pronoun to correctly complete each sentence.

   Jessie and Alycia parked _____ bikes in the tool shed.

   Brian put on _____ helmet and adjusted _____ strap.

   Mom asked, "Where are you going on _____ ride today?"

2. Use a conjunction to complete each compound sentence.

          for   or   yet   so

   It is no surprise that Lia won first
   place, _____ she is the best.

   A tree house can be a great place
   to read, _____ it can be the
   perfect place for a picnic.

3. Correctly punctuate the following sentence.

   Although it was freezing cold the family
   bundled up and went for a walk.

4. Correctly punctuate this sentence.
   (Hint: Use quotation marks.)

   Lexie answered I got my nickname from my little brother

5. **A preposition ties a noun or pronoun to other words in a
   sentence.** Find a list of prepositions in the *Help Pages*. Underline
   the prepositions. (Hint: There are three.)

   We wore our Halloween costumes and trick-or-treated at
   every house with a lighted front door on our street.

6. Write C if the underlined part states a cause; write E if the underlined part states an effect.

    _____ Many beautiful lakes were formed <u>as the result of moving and melting glaciers</u>.

    _____ <u>The melting of glaciers</u> may lead to higher water levels in the oceans.

7. Match each word with its meaning. Use what you know about Greek and Latin roots, suffixes, and prefixes or check the *Help Pages*.

    ____ postpone   ____ polymorphic   ____ phobic

    A) fearful   B) put off until later   C) many forms

8. **An adverb describes a verb. Adverbs tell *how, when, where*, or *to what extent*.** What does the adverb in this sentence tell?

    The Southland neighbors are having a yard sale tomorrow.

    when   how   where   to what extent

9. **Adding the suffix *-ly* to an adjective <u>usually</u> changes the word into an adverb.** Write the adverb formed from these adjectives.

    stupid → _____   playful → _____

    light → _____   elegant → _____

10. The adverbs in this sentence are underlined. Draw an arrow to the words they modify.

    The brown bear awoke <u>groggily</u>, but it was fishing <u>hungrily</u> in no time.

Lesson #8

1. Underline the subject pronoun and circle the object pronoun in the sentence.

   Isabel and I carried our books and returned them to the library.

2. Underline the prepositional phrase in each sentence. Double underline the preposition.

   Mom and Dad traveled throughout the Midwest. Mom bought a magnet from every state. I put them all on our refrigerator.

3. Insert a correlative conjunction pair to complete the sentence.

   Have we decided _____ we will pack a lunch

   _____ eat in the cafeteria?

4. Insert commas wherever they are needed in the sentences.

   I am taking English American History French and gym this semester.

   I would adopt an older dog from the shelter wouldn't you?

5. **The past perfect tense is formed using the helping verb _had_ and the past tense of the main verb.** Insert the <u>past perfect tense</u> of the verb listed.

   Our parents _____ us to save our money.

(advise)

   Mom compared how tall we _____ over the summer.

(grow)

   By noon we _____ the summit of Mt. Shasta.

(hike)

6. Underline each verb. Write past, present, or future to tell the tense.

   I will wash the dishes.   _____

   Max scrubs the bathtub.   _____

   Emmett fed the cats and dogs.   _____

7. Complete each sentence using the <u>present progressive tense</u> of the verb listed.

   Audrey _____ her violin.
               (practice)

   I _____ for the pizza delivery guy.
        (wait)

8. Choose the verb tense that correctly completes the sentence.

   Our teacher writes the answer on the board but (covers / covered) it before we enter.

9. Punctuate the movie titles in the sentence.

   I enjoyed Despicable Me 2 even more than Despicable Me.

10. Combine these two sentences to make a compound sentence. Use a coordinating conjunction.

    I practiced diving off the high board all summer. I am getting very good.

    _____

    _____

Lesson #9

1. **A reflexive pronoun refers back to the subject of a sentence.** Circle each reflexive pronoun and draw an arrow to the noun(s) or pronoun that it refers to.

   Ben and Ella rewarded themselves by jogging the last lap.

   We studied ourselves in the mirror.

2. Combine the two independent thoughts into a compound sentence.

   The storm caused a power outage. The power outage won't spoil our fun.

   _____

   _____

3. **A noun or pronoun that ends a prepositional phrase is called the object of a preposition.** Underline the prepositional phrase and double underline the object of the preposition in each sentence.

   I washed the glasses and put them in the cupboard.

4. **Verbs in the future perfect tense use a past tense verb with the helping verbs *will have*.** Complete the sentence using the <u>future perfect form</u> of the verb.

   Seeds planted in early May

   _____ by mid-June.
   (sprout)

5. Read the sentences. Are the underlined words *synonyms* or *antonyms*?   _____

   Mandy <u>tended</u> her garden with loving care while her brother <u>neglected</u> his. His garden soon filled with weeds.

6. Match each sentence type with an example. Add end punctuation.

   _____   There is not a cloud in the   A) interrogative
   sky today__

   _____   Put on plenty of sunscreen__   B) declarative

   _____   Yikes, the water is freezing__   C) imperative

   _____   Do you think we should sit   D) exclamatory
   under the umbrella__

7. The suffix *ful* means "full of." Match each word with its definition.

   A) mournful   B) skillful   C) harmful

   _____ full of sorrow   _____ damaging   _____ talented

8. Which of these is an example of a <u>metaphor</u>?

   A) Theresa is a lifesaver.
   B) Having Theresa around is like having an extra set of hands.
   C) I have a million things to do today!

9. What two things are being compared in the metaphor above?

   _____   _____

10. Underline the idiom in this sentence. What does the idiom mean?

   I want to buy my sister a bike, but it costs an arm and a leg.

   _____

Lesson #10

1. **An indefinite pronoun takes the place of a noun that is not specific.** Circle each indefinite pronoun and tell whether it is singular or plural.

   Example: (Many) are recycling.   _____plural_____

   I've been filling bags. Most are full already.   _____

   I bought ice cream today. Most is chocolate. _____

2. Use a correlative conjunction pair to complete the sentence.

   _____ this downpour continues, _____ we must cancel our plans to take the twins to the beach.

3. Insert commas wherever they are needed in the sentences.

   If the sun comes out we will spend the day snorkeling.

4. Circle the correct relative pronoun.

   The author (who / whom) spoke last night is from Russia.

   The person (who's / whose) hat this is must be cold.

5. **When a word ends in a *consonant* + *y* pattern, usually change the -*y* to -*i* when adding a suffix.** Rewrite each word with the suffix.

   bossy + ness → _____

   cry + ed → _____

   merry + ment → _____

6. **Do not change the *-y* to *-i* if the word ends in a *vowel* + *y* pattern.**

   obey + ed → _____

   enjoy + able → _____

   key + less → _____

7. Find these words in a thesaurus or dictionary. Underline the word that best completes the sentence.

   droll   solemn   triumphant

   The diplomat's funeral was a _____ ceremony.

8. Use editing marks to correct errors in the sentence. Write the words correctly.

   I see my orthodontist, dr. trents, on saturdays, and we get ice cream at handel's afterwards.

   _____

9. Are the underlined words *synonyms* or *antonyms*?

   Patricia is a <u>skilled</u> journalist; she is <u>proficient</u> at all types of writing.

   synonyms   antonyms

10. Match each root with its clue.

   _____ gram   A) light

   _____ phon   B) sound

   _____ photo   C) written

Lesson #11

1. Circle the verb that correctly completes the sentence. Underline the antecedent that tells if the indefinite pronoun is singular or plural.

   I baked fourteen loaves, and more (is / are) in the oven.

   I kneaded the dough for rye bread. More (is / are) in the freezer.

2. Combine the two independent thoughts into a compound sentence.

   Florida is a peninsula. Its name means "full of flowers."

   _____

   _____

3. Underline each prepositional phrase and double underline each object of the preposition in the following sentence.

   Levi ate his lunch under the tree between two houses.

4. Complete these sentences using the <u>present perfect tense</u> of the verb *walk*.

   The ants _____ away with our watermelon.

   Aurora _____ to school many times.

5. Match each past verb tense with a sentence.

   A) past perfect   B) simple past   C) past progressive

   _____ The firemen showed us how to install smoke detectors.

   _____ The saleslady was showing us ways to lace our tennis shoes.

   _____ Our teachers had shown us the fire exits many times.

6. Which sentence has an incorrect shift (error) in verb tense?

_____ Lewis and Clark explored the Northwest Territory and studied its plants and animals.

_____ Lewis and Clark explored the Northwest Territory and study its plants and animals.

7. Correctly punctuate the movie title in this sentence.

Our dog looks just like Winn-Dixie from the movie Because of Winn-Dixie.

8. Choose the word that has the most positive connotation.

The (odor / scent / smell) of my grandmother's perfume was a familiar one.

9. Underline the complete subject and double underline the complete predicate.

Four juicy peaches were hanging on a branch just out of our reach.

Write the simple subject. _____

Write the simple predicate. _____

10. Choose the best subordinating conjunction to complete each sentence.

because   unless   except   until

Maureen loves all the candy _____ chocolate covered cherries.

Paul made the golf team _____ his score was the lowest.

Lesson #12

1. Read the sentence below. Choose the meaning of the underlined word.

    The text message was <u>ambiguous</u>, so Clarice was uncertain what the sender was asking.

    A) obvious
    B) sent more than once
    C) having more than one meaning

2. Look at the table of Greek and Latin roots in the *Help Pages.* Match each of the Greek and Latin roots with its meaning.

    _____ pan   A) heat

    _____ thermo   B) first

    _____ prim   C) all

3. Find the meaning and pronunciation of the word *indigenous* in a dictionary. Place a check next to the statement that is true.

    _____ *Foreign* is a synonym of *indigenous.*
    _____ *Indigenous* is an adjective.
    _____ *Indigenous* is a way of making holes.
    _____ All are true.

4. Proofread the sentence below. Use spelling, capitalization, and punctuation symbols to mark any errors.

    Patrick and i wrote about the many

    noticable improvments that were

    made on the hiking trail this Fall

5. Underline the complete subject. Circle the simple predicate.

    Shade-loving flowers grow nicely near the tree line.

6. Fill in the correct word to complete each sentence. Choose *they're*, *their*, or *there*.

   Have the players picked _____ captain yet?

   Do I leave my ballot here or over _____?

   _____ not announcing the winner until after practice.

7. Underline the relative pronoun; circle its antecedent.

   The musician who lives next door is performing with the Metropolitan Opera tonight.

8. Fill in the second half of the correlative conjunction pair in each sentence.

   Either you have time to help me, _____ I will ask someone else.

   If this job is too big, _____ ask Marty for help.

9. Add the suffixes to each word. Write the new words.

	-able	-ment
manage	_____	_____
enforce	_____	_____
contain	_____	_____

10. Underline the figure of speech.

    The ball rolled straight as an arrow toward the remaining pins.

    What two things are being compared?

    _____   _____

Lesson #13

1. Circle the verb that agrees with the indefinite pronoun. Underline the antecedent that determines whether the indefinite pronoun is singular or plural.

   I looked at the socks in my top drawer. All (is / are) knee socks.

   I got money for my birthday! Most (is / are) in my bank account.

2. Choose the meaning of the underlined word.

   Molly remained a <u>conundrum</u> to Matthew since she never acted the same way from one day to the next.

        puzzle   transparent   well understood

3. Underline the adverb. Draw an arrow to the word it modifies.

   Jackson is traveling tomorrow to see her.

4. Identify the part of speech of the homograph in each sentence.

   Henry painted <u>minute</u> pictures on the heads of thumbtacks.

        noun (**mĭn** ĭt)   adjective (mī **noot**)

   It took Chantel a little over a <u>minute</u> to pick out a movie.

        noun (**mĭn** ĭt)   adjective (mī **noot**)

5. Underline the part that states a cause.

   Tony mows lawns and walks dogs around his neighborhood since he needs to earn money to repair his bicycle.

6. Insert correct punctuation.

   Wow she baked cookies muffins cupcakes
   and brownies for the team picnic

7. What part of speech is each underlined word?

   The <u>American</u> <u>astronaut</u> <u>repaired</u> the <u>telescope</u>, <u>so</u> it could
         1   2   3   4   5

   photograph earth.

   _____ coordinating conjunction
   _____ subject
   _____ proper adjective
   _____ direct object
   _____ verb

8. The root *hydro* means "water." Match each word with its clue.

   hydrosphere   fear of water

   hydrophobia   water-powered electricity production

   hydroelectric   water layer on earth

9. Cross out any misspelled words. Spell them correctly on the line.

   potatos   reciept   neighbor   happyness

   _____

10. Underline the verb phrase. Identify the tense.

    Vickie has walked the entire Appalachian Trail twice.

    present progressive   present perfect   past progressive

Lesson #14

1. Look at the table of Greek and Latin roots in the *Help Pages*. Match each root below with its meaning.

   _____ con   A) with

   _____ mal   B) half

   _____ hemi   C) bad

2. Find these words in a thesaurus or dictionary. Underline the word that best completes the sentence.

   tenacious   unreliable   dilapidated

   Emily scored after dribbling the ball the length of the field, showing her _____ side.

3. Fill in the correct word to complete the sentence. Choose two, to, or too.

   It is up _____ Mom to decide which of the _____

   coats doesn't cost _____ much money.

4. Choose the verb tense that correctly completes the sentence.

   Brian handily tosses the ball to Matt, but he barely (catches / caught) it.

5. Complete these sentences using the <u>future progressive tense</u>.

   Jason _____ back to school soon. (drive)

   He _____ for dinner at Grandma's. (stop)

6. Choose the correct pronoun.

   My grandmother (that / who) fell and broke her hip is in the hospital.

7. Underline the correlative conjunction pair in each sentence.

   We play not only beach volleyball, but also badminton.

   If we set up the space for one game, then we can also play the other.

   Neither the guide nor the climbers reached the summit.

8. Match the underlined word in each sentence to the correct part of speech.

   _____ preposition A) You are going <u>next</u>!

   _____ adverb B) <u>Next</u> year, I'll be able to vote.

   _____ adjective C) Troy left the mail <u>next</u> to the phone.

9. Insert adverbs to complete this sentence.

   quick   quickly   slow   slowly

   When the music sped up, the ballerinas danced _____, and when the music slowed, they danced _____.

10. Underline the complete subject and double underline the complete predicate.

    The tiny stray kitten lapped up all the milk in the bowl.

    Write the simple subject. _____

    Write the simple predicate. _____

Lesson #15

1. Circle the verb that correctly completes each sentence.

    Every girl worked hard to help the team win the championship. Each (is / are) receiving a trophy.

    My friends really want to go to the concert. Several (is / are) already in line to buy tickets.

2. Find the word *evident* in a thesaurus or dictionary. Underline a synonym.

    mistaken   suspicious   clear   dangerous

3. Insert correct punctuation.

    My favorite activities at camp are kayaking painting kickball and swimming

4. Choose the correct relative pronoun. Draw an arrow to its antecedent.

    The first site (that / whose) we chose for our campfire was unacceptable because it was too close to dry leaves.

5. Insert correct punctuation.

    Yes Phillip and I learned the best ways to completely extinguish a campfire.

    It is a very important camping skill don't you agree?

6. Underline the part of the sentence that is the effect.

    Marcus couldn't find his way around his new town, so he made himself a map of his important destinations.

7. Underline the idiom. What does it mean?

   Jacob knew if he was going to pass the test, he would have to hit the books.

   ___ change the numbers   ___ study

   ___ throw textbooks around   ___ punch a punching bag

8. Read the sentences. Cross out the fragment. Rewrite the fragment as a sentence on the line.

   Kyle joined the scouts to do many fun things with the troop. Camping, hiking, orienteering, and more. He is going canoeing with the rest of the boys on Saturday.

   _____

   _____

9. Use proofreader's symbols to edit errors in the sentences below. Write the words correctly.

   marcus put the Library and the swiming pool on his map. He labeled it springfield, ohio and dated it september 15, 2015.

   _____

10. **Interjections express emotion. They can stand alone or be used within a sentence. When part of a sentence, they are set off by commas. An exclamation mark is appropriate also.**

    Place the correct punctuation around the interjection in each sentence.

    Wait__ it is not your turn.

    Help__ My grandmother has fallen.

Lesson #16

1. Choose the verb that agrees with the singular indefinite pronoun.

   Neither of the sisters (was / were) old enough to baby sit.

2. Look at the table of Greek and Latin roots in the *Help Pages*. Match each root below with its meaning.

   _____ pro   A) law

   _____ sub   B) for

   _____ jus   C) below

3. Find the word *complaisant* in a thesaurus or dictionary. Which of these means the same as *complaisant*?

   obstinate   agreeable   embarrassed   talented

4. **All three perfect verb tenses use past tense verbs plus the helping verbs *had, has, have*, or *will have*.** Complete the chart for the verbs listed; use the subject *we*.

	Present Perfect	Past Perfect	Future Perfect
fix	have fixed	had fixed	
sing			will have sung
forget	have forgotten		

5. Rewrite the sentence with correct capitalization and punctuation.

   the frog prince is one of the short stories we were assigned from the book a treasury of fairy tales.

   _____

   _____

6. Keep the verbs in present tense. Cross out the incorrect verb and write it correctly on the line.

   At 5:00 p.m. Mom prepares dinner, Dad walked the dog, and we finish our homework. _____

7. Complete the correlative conjunction pair in each sentence.

   If we don't want to be late, _____ we had better get up early.

   The parade will include not only twenty floats _____ five high school bands.

8. Fill in the <u>past progressive tense</u> of the verb *extinguish*.

   The firemen _____ _____ the fire when the explosion occurred.

9. Match each sentence type with an example of it. Add the end punctuation.

   _____ declarative   A) Do you want to learn how to
                                 water ski__

   _____ interrogative   B) Put on a life jacket__

   _____ imperative   C) You can go first__

   _____ exclamatory   D) Oh no, I hope that is not a
                                 shark's fin__

10. Draw a line to match these prefixes with their meanings.

    pre-   after

    inter-   between

    post-   before

Lesson #17

1. Use proofreader's symbols to correct the capitalization errors in this sentence.

   Brian and his Mom sailed over the aegean sea to istanbul, the capital of turkey.

2. **An effect happens after a cause, but the effect may come first in a sentence.** Put a C if the underlined words state a cause or an E if they state an effect.

   _____ Alexie went to a salon since she needed a haircut.

   _____ Alexie cried because the salon cut her hair too short!

3. In each sentence, underline the verb that shows action that is ongoing or continues. Indicate if it is past, present or future progressive.

   William is packing his suitcase for a trip to his uncle's farm.

   _____ progressive.

   He will be spending more than two weeks with them.

   _____ progressive.

4. Read the sentence. Are the underlined words synonyms or antonyms?

   Cargo from the overturned boat was <u>salvaged</u>; even the baskets were <u>recovered</u>.

   synonyms   antonyms

5. Underline the complete subject and double underline the complete predicate.

   The rescue helicopter lifted the victims out of the choppy waters.

6. Match each word to a part of the *i before e except after c or when sounding like 'a'* spelling rule.

        A) deceive   B) yield   C) freight

    _____ *i* before e   _____ except after c

    _____ or when sounding like 'a'

7. Insert commas where needed in each sentence.

I need balloons candles a piñata and crepe paper.

Five bags of candy should fit in the piñata don't you think?

8. Underline the idiom in the sentence below. Which statement captures the meaning of the idiom?

We wanted to ask the principal for more recess time. Since we had misbehaved, our teacher said not to rock the boat.

    _____ risk tipping the boat over in rough water

    _____ disrupt a satisfactory situation

9. Fill in the table; use the subject *they* and the verb *sleep*.

past perfect	present perfect	future perfect

10. Use a conjunction to join two sentences into one.

We wanted to take the bus into town. The bus was already full.

_____

_____

Lesson #18

1. Are the underlined words synonyms or antonyms?

   I was worried my teachers would <u>admonish</u> me for the prank. Truth be told, I deserved a good <u>reprimand</u>.

   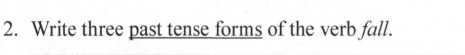

          synonyms   antonyms

2. Write three <u>past tense forms</u> of the verb *fall*.

past	past progressive	past perfect
	was	had

3. Look at the table of Greek and Latin roots in the *Help Pages*. Match each root below with its meaning.

   _____ hydro   A) around

   _____ circum   B) time

   _____ chrono   C) water

4. Find the meaning and pronunciation of the word *implicit* in a dictionary. Place a check next to any statement that is true.

   _____ means "understood without being stated"
   _____ rhymes with reincite
   _____ is an adjective
   _____ All are true.

5. Underline the idiom in the sentence below. Which statement captures the meaning of the idiom?

   If we are going to design a mass transit system for this town, we will have to think outside the box.

   _____ go outside of a square office or classroom space

   _____ approach a problem in new and novel ways

6. Choose the correct relative pronoun. Draw an arrow to its antecedent.

   The book _____ Miss Hunt recommended is on your desk.

   that   whom   whose

7. Choose from the list of possessive pronouns to correctly complete each sentence.

   our   her   his   its
   ours   theirs   their   it's

   The West River overflowed _____banks.

   Tom and Judy rode _____ bikes to school.

   They forgot _____ so we lent them one of _____.

8. Add commas where needed.

   Since they found the skeleton, the boys have been interviewed by the governor of our state the mayor of our town and several news crews.

9. Underline the correlative conjunction pair in each sentence.

   We will leave tomorrow whether the roads are clear or snow covered.

   For the sleepover, she ordered not only pizza but also chicken wings.

10. Correctly punctuate the title of the website.

    Mr. Trenton let us play geometry games on Coolmath4kids before taking our math quiz.

Lesson #19

1. Choose the verbs that agree with the indefinite pronouns.

   I used all the flour from this sack. I hope more (is / are) in the cupboard. I collected all the pennies from my room and yours. Do you think more (is / are) in the kitchen?

2. Circle the helping verb; draw an M over the main verb.

   Morgan can go with us to the shore.

3. Fill in the appropriate form of the <u>present progressive tense</u>.

   Victoria and her friends _____ _____ this weekend. (ski)

   Christopher _____ _____ old friends. (visit)

4. Draw a line through the fragment.

   Felicity began stringing beads and charms in the third grade. Rubber band and friendship bracelets. Felicity gives the bracelets to her sisters and her classmates.

   What is missing from the fragment?   noun   verb   both

5. Choose the correct word.

   You behaved (good / well) in the restaurant.

   What part of speech is it?   _____

6. Choose the correlative conjunctions that best complete the sentence.

   either/or   not only/but also   as/as

   Renee gathered _____ many

   wildflowers _____ she could hold.

7. Add commas and quotation marks.

    That's a great idea, and we'll have time if we get
    started now added Henrique.

8. **The helping verb *could* is the past tense of *can*. It is
    also used with a main verb to show possibility or ask
    permission.**

    Examples: *possibility*   The dog could be outside.

    past tense of can   He could always ski better
    than his classmates.

    question / permission   Could you lend me money
    for lunch?

    Underline the verb phrase in each sentence. Tell how *could* is used.

    A) possibility   B) question   C) past tense of can

    _____ Could you help me find my keys?

    _____ This could be your last chance.

    _____ We could see the train rounding the bend.

9. **An adjective that states an *opinion* usually comes <u>before</u> an
    adjective that tells *color*.** Choose adjectives to complete the
    sentence.

              green   scratchy   pink   delicate

    Jenelle hung her _____ _____ tutu on a hanger.

    Micah preferred not to wear the _____ _____
    scarf.

10. Underline the adverb. Draw an arrow to the word it modifies.

    We're going to the museum tomorrow.

Lesson #20

1. **The helping verb *would* is the past tense of *will*. It also may ask for something or express a wish.**

   Examples: *past tense of* will   Mondays we would meet for coffee.

        question   Would you ask if I could come along?

        wish   Mom, Jonas would like another cookie.

   Underline the verb phrase in each sentence. Tell how *would* is used.

       A) wish   B) question   C) past tense of *will*

   _____ On weekends we would go to Grandma's for dinner.

   _____ I would prefer tea, thank you.

   _____ Would it be all right if I finished this tomorrow?

2. Correctly rewrite the fragment as a complete sentence.

   Exploded in a burst of color over our backyard.

   _____

   _____

3. Underline two complete thoughts and circle a coordinating conjunction in the compound sentence.

   I ordered an extra-large ice cream cone, but most of it dripped down my arm.

4. Write the past tense irregular verb to complete the sentence. You can find a list of irregular verbs in the *Help Pages*.

   The ground _____, and the wind _____.
          (freeze)   (blow)

5. Look at the table of Greek and Latin roots in the *Help Pages*. Match each root below with its meaning.

   A) again   B) opposite   C) out of

   _____ ex   _____ il   _____ re

6. Find these words in a thesaurus or dictionary. Underline the word that best completes the sentence.

   discontinue   inherent   persevere

   To break the long distance swimming record, Ethan had to _____ another fifteen minutes.

7. Underline the complete subject and double underline the complete predicate.

   Everyone in the back row screamed at the same moment.

8. Underline the relative pronoun; circle its antecedent.

   The driver whose car was in the repair shop took the bus.

9. Underline the prepositional phrase. Circle the object of the preposition.

   The enormous orange moon hovered over the horizon.

10. Keep the verbs in past tense. Cross out the incorrect verb and write it correctly on the line.

   The trick-or-treaters open their bags and Cristina filled them with mini candy bars and coins.

   _____

Lesson #21

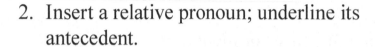

1. Circle the subject and underline the verb in the following sentences.

   Knights defended the castle.

   They were strong and brave.

2. Insert a relative pronoun; underline its antecedent.

   The student to _____ they gave an award for artistic creativity is my neighbor.

3 – 5. Use the graphic organizer to sort the adjectives in the table into categories.

silly	pink	circular	younger	round	likeable
kind	dozen	turquoise	lazy	single	square
gigantic	ancient	tasty	black	elderly	two
triangular	five	happy	tiny	purple	immense

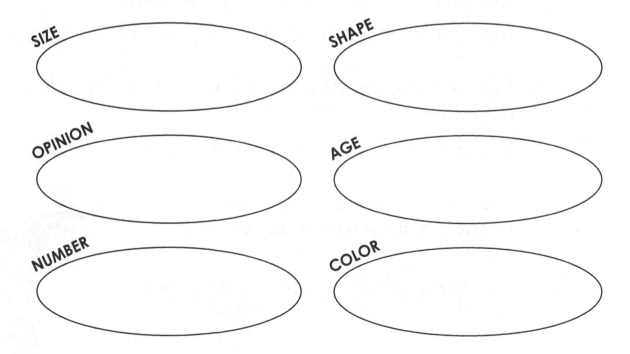

SIZE

SHAPE

OPINION

AGE

NUMBER

COLOR

6. Complete the sentence. Choose the <u>future progressive form</u> of the verb.

    The twins _____ together.

    study   are studying   will be studying   have studied

7. The helping verb *should* plus a main verb suggests "probably" or "supposed to." Match each sentence to the way *should* is being used in the sentence.

    _____ supposed to   A) It should stop raining soon.

    _____ probably will   B) You should wear boots when you muck out the horses' stalls.

8. Insert a comma in the sentence.

    Roberto won two gold medals in swimming but he did not break a world record.

9. Underline the prepositions in these word groups. Circle the object of the preposition.

    throughout the year

    above the deep blue sea

    around the last sharp bend

10. Underline the complete thought and double underline the incomplete thought in this complex sentence. Circle the subordinating conjunction.

    I brought you a gift since your birthday is next month.

Lesson #22

1. Match each sentence with the way *can* is used.

   _____ able to   A) Mom said I can go over to
                              Tessa's house.

   _____ permission to   B) The river can flood the
                              underpass if it keeps raining.

   _____ willing to   C) I can take that to the office for
                              you.

   _____ possibility of   D) I can run faster than everyone
                              in my gym class.

2. **Adjectives tell *size*, *shape*, *age*, *color*, and *number*. A word that states *an opinion* about a noun is also an adjective. Underline the adjectives that state *an opinion*.**

   The short ungrateful child did not eat her delicious supper.

3. Underline the independent clause and double underline the dependent clause. Circle the subordinating conjunction.

   Sabrina popped a big bowl of popcorn before
   we sat down to watch the movie.

4. Find these words in a thesaurus or dictionary.
   Underline the word that best completes the sentence.

        prismatic   orb   tableau

   The full moon appeared as a perfect, luminous _____
   in the night sky.

5. Underline any words that are <u>not</u> synonyms of the word *ignorance*.

        knowledgeable   proficient   unaware

        educated   unintelligent   oblivious

6. Punctuate the interjection.

   Wow It is almost midnight.

7. Is each underlined word an adverb or a preposition?

   Follow this street <u>around</u> the corner.

   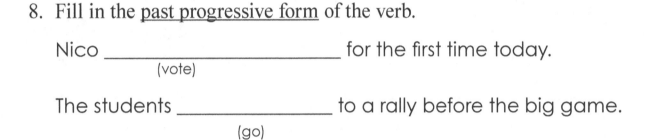

          adverb   preposition

   Tony and Maria went to the park and walked
   <u>around</u>.

          adverb   preposition

8. Fill in the <u>past progressive form</u> of the verb.

   Nico _____ for the first time today.
                (vote)

   The students _____ to a rally before the big game.
                (go)

9. Correctly punctuate the titles of creative works.

   My big sister loved to play Candy Crush online with her
   friends over summer break. My younger sister liked to read
   books; her favorite that summer was Bud, Not Buddy. I
   wrote poems about nature, and my poem Friendzzzzz was
   published in a teen magazine.

10. Underline the idiom.

    Today I was elected class president. I couldn't wait to tell
    my family, but Harper stole my thunder by announcing she
    heard my opponent's concession speech.

    What does it mean?   _____

Lesson #23

1. Sort the pronouns and write each one in the proper list.

    few   our   that   somebody   who

    everyone   which   my   many

    Indefinite _____

    Relative _____

    Possessive _____

2. Complete the sentence. Choose the <u>present progressive form</u> of the verb.

    Alycia _____ into her costume for the parade.

    changed   will be changing   is changing   changes

3. Match each sentence to the way in which *could* is being used.

    _____ is able   A) Dad is the only one who could repair the roof.

    _____ possibility   B) If we go to Florida, Alex could watch our dogs.

4. **An adjective that states an opinion usually comes <u>before</u> an adjective that tells shape.** Correctly insert the adjectives in the sentence.

    round   glittery

    A _____ _____ emerald hung from her neck.

5. Insert a relative pronoun; underline its antecedent.

    The actors _____ want to audition
    need to schedule an appointment.

6. Draw a line through the fragment.

    The local ice cream store sells many unusual flavors.
    Pistachio, cheese strudel, hazelnut, and bubble gum.
    Four times a month they feature a new flavor.

    Rewrite the fragment as a complete thought.

    _____

    _____

7. Find the meaning and pronunciation of the word *gaunt* in a
    dictionary. Place a ✓ next to any statement that is true.

    _____ *Gaunt* rhymes with *haunt*.

    _____ The word *gaunt* is a verb.

    _____ The opposite of *gaunt* is *plump*.

8. Underline the interrogative pronouns.

    What is your phone number, and where do you live?

9. Underline the prepositional phrase. Double underline the object of
    the preposition.

    Todd and I maneuvered our boat around the bend.

10. Does the underlined part state a cause or an effect? cause effect

    <u>Mom took a group of us to the movies</u> since it had been
    raining every day.

Lesson #24

1. **When forming the future tense, use the helping verb *would* in place of *will* if there is a condition that prevents an action from happening.**

   Examples: Action is going to happen:
   He *will* come to the bungee demonstration.

   A condition prevents the action from happening:
   I *would* go to the movies, but I don't have a ride.

   Match each example with the way *will* and *would* are used.

   _____ action will happen

   _____ a condition prevents the action from happening

   A) I would take your picture, but I lost my camera.

   B) I will buy a new camera today.

2. **Use the helping verb *would* to form the past tense of *will*. *Would* is also used with a main verb to be polite.**

   Examples:

   past tense of *will*: When I was late, I would eat an apple for breakfast.

   polite: I would love a second cup of tea.

   Match each example with the way *would* is used.

   _____ past tense of *will*   A) I would take this road often.

   _____ polite   B) Would you please call tomorrow?

3. Complete the sentence.

   A) coordinating conjunction   B) subordinating conjunction

   A complex sentence has a complete thought and an incomplete thought with a _____.

4. Use what you know about the root *cent* to make the best choice. What has a *centenarian* done?

   A) written a book   C) lived for 100 years

   B) crossed an ocean   D) been elected to government

5. Circle the prepositions and underline the objects of the prepositions in each sentence.

The Environmental Club picked up litter along the main streets.

The dogs bounded through the fields and into the river.

6. Complete the sentence by writing the <u>present perfect tense</u> of the verb.

Troy and Amelia _____ blue ribbons in dance.
                         (win)

7. Fill in the <u>present progressive tense</u> of the verb.

Ethan _____ the car for us.
             (wash)

8. Which sentence has an incorrect shift (error) in verb tense?

_____ Sheila knocks on the door and walked in.

_____ Sheila knocked on the door and walked in.

9. Circle the word that completes the correlative conjunction pair.

I will watch either a movie (or / not only / and) television.

10. Punctuate the sentence correctly.

Violet tossed greens carrots broccoli celery and pears in a salad fit for a king.

Lesson #25

1. Insert a relative pronoun; underline its antecedent.

   The hungry, wet dog _____ was found out in the cold is sleeping now.

2. Match each example with the way *will* and *would* are used.

   _____ action will happen

   _____ a condition prevents the action from happening

   _____ past tense of *will*

   _____ polite

   A) Would you walk the dog today?

   B) He will shop there again.

   C) They would come with us, but their spring break is at a different time.

   D) I remember how I would row across the lake on weekend mornings.

3. Correctly rewrite the fragment below as a complete sentence.

   The French Club is going to visit the Eiffel Tower when it is in Paris this summer. Also, take a cruise and go to Notre Dame. I wish I had taken French.

   _____

4. Choose the correct words to complete the sentence.

   If you study how the sun's (raise / rays) help plants make their own food, you might be able to (raise / rays) your grade.

5. Insert the <u>present perfect form</u> of the verb *mistake*. (If you're not sure, check the *Help Pages*.)

   I think someone may _____ my suitcase for his.

6. Complete the sentence by writing the <u>future perfect tense</u> of the verb.

Before the Olympics are over, the competing nations _____ many games.
(play)

7. Rewrite each word with the suffix.

arrange + *ment*   _____

fancy + *ful*   _____

love + *able*   _____

loyal + *ly*   _____

8. Add three commas to this sentence.

Farmer Jean composts leftover corn lettuce carrots and tomatoes.

9. Use a conjunction to make these two independent thoughts into one sentence. Punctuate correctly.

Dr. Fisher is my dentist. Dr. Richards is my orthodontist.

_____

_____

10. Add an apostrophe, commas, quotation marks, and an end mark.

Lets walk to the skateboard park suggested Erica. We can get an ice cream cone on the way home she added

Lesson #26

1. Choose the correct relative pronoun. Circle its antecedent.

   The book _____ I choose for my report was a Newbury Award winner.

              that   whom   whose

2. Complete the sentence. Choose the <u>past progressive form</u> of the verb.

   Tall waves _____ the lighthouse during our visit.

      pounded   had pounded   pound   were pounding

3. **The helping verb *should* plus a main verb suggests "probably" or "supposed to."** Match how *should* is used with the example.

   _____ supposed to   A) The train should arrive soon.

   _____ probably   B) The doctor said we really should eat an apple a day.

4. Sort these words into two categories.

      greedily   muggy   lazily   shady   mysteriously   hungry

   Adverbs _____

   Adjectives _____

5. Punctuate the title of the movie.

   I saw E.T. the Extra-Terrestrial for the third time.

6. Read the sentence. Let's talk about the movie.

   What does the preposition do?

   A) acts as a verb   C) acts as the subject
   B) relates talk to movie   D) takes the place of a noun

7. Complete the sentence by writing the <u>past perfect tense</u> of the verb.

   The birds _____ all the seeds in the feeder.
                        (eat)

   Vincenzo _____ enough pasta for a large party.
                       (prepare)

8. Irregular plural nouns do not end in –s. Write the plural of each noun.

   child _____   person _____

   goose _____   ox _____

9. Which sentence has correct verb agreement?

   _____ Last winter there were many
         blue jays in our back yard, and
         we take their picture every day.

   _____ Last winter there were many
         blue jays in our back yard, and
         we took their picture every day.

10. Insert a comma in each sentence.

    I couldn't eat another bite could you?

    Yes I would love to go again.

Lesson #27

1. **The helping verb *may* asks for permission.**

   Match each sentence with the way *may* is used.

   _____ possibility   A) Chad may stop over tonight.

   _____ permission   B) May we go next door to see
                                 Arabella's new puppy?

2. **An adjective that states an opinion usually comes <u>before</u> an adjective that tells age.** Correctly insert the adjectives in each sentence.

   old   crunchy   Crumbs fell to the floor as the dog chewed
                       the _____ _____ bone.

   delicate   new   One _____ _____
                       blossom bloomed on the orchid every day.

3. Circle the complete subject and underline the complete predicate in the following sentence.

   Leonardo Da Vinci, a great inventor, designed a submarine and a helicopter in the 1400s.

4. Choose the correct words to complete the sentence.

   Cut the (bored / board) precisely the first time, and I won't get (bored / board) while I wait for you to recut it.

5. Underline the cause in each sentence.

   Merrill needed stitches after she fell on the playground.

   To celebrate Tim's birthday, we are going to dinner.

6. Use proofreader's symbols to mark the errors in the sentence.

   My favorite Amusement park it is cedar point in ohio because it has the best roller coasters

7. Study the chart; choose one of the examples to match with each clue.

Root	Meaning	Examples
post	after	postdate, postpone
anti	against	antifreeze, antibiotic
pre	before	precooked, pretest

put off until later _____

to test beforehand _____

to prevent freezing _____

8. Is the demonstrative in the sentences used as a *pronoun* or an *adjective*?

This is delicious.   pronoun adjective

These tennis shoes fit me perfectly.   pronoun adjective

I read that book when it first came out.   pronoun adjective

9. Identify the verb tense of each sentence.

    A) past perfect   B) present perfect   C) future perfect

_____ The chef has prepared 400 meatballs for the spaghetti dinner fundraiser.

_____ Aurora will have hiked the Buckeye Trail four times.

10. Underline the idiom in this sentence.

Since it was my birthday, my favorite restaurant said my dessert was on the house.

What does the idiom mean?   _____

Lesson #28

1. Underline a complete thought and double underline an incomplete thought. Circle the subordinating conjunction.

    Since Ricky was almost sixteen, he began to take driving lessons.

2. Insert a relative pronoun; underline its antecedent.

    All of the sailors _____ wanted to sail with Christopher Columbus met on the Santa Maria.

3. Complete the sentence by writing the adjectives in the correct order. See the *Help Pages* if you are not sure which should come first.

    rectangular   chewy

    Only two of the _____ _____ brownies were left on the plate.

    twenty-four   oval

    The tree was surrounded by _____ _____ stones.

4. Use the meaning of the underlined part of the word to select the correct definition of each word.

    _____ <u>pede</u>strian   A) something that is transferred

    _____ <u>mal</u>practice   B) one who walks

    _____ <u>trans</u>mission   C) wrong or negligent action

5. Underline two antonyms in this sentence.

    Even though the race had left Chloe totally exhausted, she was energized by the applauding fans at the finish line.

6. Add proper punctuation — commas, quotation marks, an apostrophe, and an end mark — to complete this sentence.

   I havent called Marissa Hannah or Louisa since I lost my phone Henry explained

7. Choose the best correlative conjunction pair to complete the sentence.

   either / or   not only / but also   whether / or

   My younger sister _____ won the spelling bee for

   her grade _____ finished first in an essay contest.

8. Which sentence is punctuated correctly?

   _____ Of course Skip is the best goalie, don't you think?
   _____ Of course, Skip is the best goalie, don't you think?
   _____ Of course, Skip is the best goalie don't you think?

9. Use context clues to choose the meaning of the underlined word.

   Every night at dusk, a few tourists would come to watch the exodus of thousands of bats leaving their mountainside cave.

   arrival   landing   departure   vacation

10. Complete the chart. Use a dictionary.

	Part of Speech	Meaning
ingenious		
persevere		
enigma		

Lesson #29

1. Complete the sentence by writing the adjectives in the correct order.

         miniature   shiny   four

   Aunt Hattie arranged the _____ _____

   _____ chairs around the table in her dollhouse

   dining room.

2. Choose the correct words to complete the sentence.

   Chad had to go (threw / through) the garbage after he
   accidentally (threw / through) away his brother's model car.

   Marco used (coarse / course) sandpaper on a birdhouse for
   his beginning woodworking (coarse / course).

3. Complete the sentence by adding the <u>present perfect
   tense</u> of the verb *borrow*.

   The fifth graders _____ all the
   library books they need for their research.

4. Is each underlined word an adverb or a preposition?

   Our new dog likes to bury his bones <u>below</u> his
   doghouse.

            adverb   preposition

   The upper deck of the ferry was full so we went <u>below</u>.

            adverb   preposition

5. Underline the relative pronoun; circle its antecedent.

   The singer whose song won a Grammy Award is performing
   at Blossom Music Center.

6. Use editing marks to correct the errors.

   is the pizza which you ordered arriving before noon

7. Is the underlined part of the sentence a metaphor or a simile?

   After she won the gold medal her face was as *radiant* <u>as a ray of sunshine</u>.

   metaphor   simile

   Using context clues, write a synonym for *radiant*. _____

8. Fill in the <u>future progressive tense form</u> of the verb.

   Gemma _____ all the way to New York City.
   (drive)

   The teachers _____ the third graders before lunch.
   (test)

9. Add commas to the series in this sentence.

   My favorite holidays are Thanksgiving Day Valentine's Day and Halloween.

10. Punctuate the titles in the sentence.

    The New Kid on the Block is a book of funny poetry that includes the poem I Wonder Why Dad Is So Thoroughly Mad.

Lesson #30

1. Complete the sentence. Write the <u>present progressive form</u> of the verb *practice*.

   The swim team _____ in the community pool today.

   All the divers _____ their most difficult dives.

2. Complete the sentence by writing the adjectives in the correct order.

   dozen   brown   tiny

   A _____ _____ _____ birds chirped around the newly-filled feeders.

3. Is the underlined word an adverb or a preposition?

   The fire department came to rescue the kitty, but it had already jumped <u>down</u>.

   adverb   preposition

4. Draw a line through the fragment.

   If I had a time machine, I would travel back to the age of knights. I would learn to be a jousting expert. A dragon slayer!

   What is missing from the fragment?

   subject   verb   both

5. What does the underlined saying mean?

   Mom <u>put her foot down</u>; she would no longer allow Jason to go to practice unless his homework was done.

   stamped her foot   took firm action   tried on new shoes

6. Use the meaning of the underlined part of the word to select the correct definition of each word.

_____ <u>micro</u>chip   A) self-acting or acting on its own

_____ <u>il</u>literate   B) not knowing how to read or write

_____ <u>auto</u>nomic   C) a group of tiny electronic circuits

7. Read the sentence. Underline the figure of speech. Is it a simile or a metaphor?

The next competitor is a machine on skates!

    simile   metaphor

8. Underline two adverbs in this sentence.

Today Lola ran faster than Ellie's best time.

9. Underline the relative pronoun in each sentence. Draw an arrow to its antecedent.

These are my friends who go to a climbing gym.

The dog that ate the bag of cookies is not feeling very well.

10. Punctuate each sentence.

In spite of being warned I forgot my homework again

Yes I think Steve did pick up the recycling didn't he

Common Core
ENGLISH GRAMMAR 5
& Mechanics

Help Pages

Some material addressed in standards covered at earlier grade levels
may not be available in these *Help Pages*, but you can access all grade levels
of *Simple Solutions Common Core English Grammar & Mechanics Help Pages* at
SimpleSolutions.org.

Help Pages

Eight Parts of Speech

Adjective	describes a noun or pronoun
Adverb	describes a verb, adjective, or another adverb
Conjunction	connects words or phrases in a sentence
Interjection	a word or short phrase that shows emotion
Noun	names a person, place, or thing
Preposition	relates a noun or pronoun to other words in a sentence
Pronoun	takes the place of a noun
Verb	shows action or a state of being

Parts of Speech - Nouns

A **common noun** names a person, place, thing, or idea. A **proper noun** names a particular person, place, thing or idea. A proper noun begins with a capital letter. Nouns may be singular or plural.

Some of the Functions of Nouns

Subject	The subject is whom or what the sentence is about. ***Example***: <u>Tom</u> likes to play piano.
Direct Object	A direct object receives the action of the verb. ***Example***: Tom plays the <u>piano</u>. To find the DO, ask: Tom plays what?
Object of a Preposition	The object of a preposition comes at the end of a prepositional phrase. ***Example***: Mr. Gore plays in an <u>orchestra</u>.
Predicate Nominative (Predicate Noun)	A predicate nominative renames the subject. ***Example***: Tom and Mr. Gore are <u>musicians</u>.
Possessive	A possessive noun shows ownership and usually modifies another noun. ***Examples***: <u>Mr. Gore's</u> class uses <u>Tom's</u> piano.
Collective	A collective noun names a group (Ex. *team*, *family*, *herd*, *flock*). A collective noun is singular and takes a singular verb. ***Example***: The <u>family</u> enjoy<u>s</u> camping.

Parts of Speech - Pronouns

A **pronoun** takes the place of a noun. The noun that the pronoun is referring to is called the **antecedent**. The antecedent is in the same sentence or a recent, earlier sentence; occasionally, an antecedent is not specifically named. It is implied, or "understood."

Examples: The <u>puppy</u> is in <u>its</u> pen.
                ("<u>its</u> pen" refers to the puppy's pen, so "puppy" is the antecedent.)
                <u>It</u> has been raining all day.
                (There is no clear antecedent, but we know "it" refers to the weather.)

Help Pages

Types of Pronouns	
Case	**Personal Pronouns**
Subjective	Used as the subject of a sentence or clause *Singular*: I, you, he/she, it *Plural*: we, you, they
Objective	Used as an object; found in the predicate of a sentence *Singular*: me, you, him/her, it *Plural*: us, you, them
Possessive	Used to show ownership; modify nouns *Singular*: my, mine*, your, yours*, his*, her, hers*, its* *Plural*: our, ours*, your, yours*, their, theirs*, whose * These can stand alone.

Other Types of Pronouns	
Indefinite	Replaces a noun that is not specific *Example*: <u>Someone</u> is knocking. (*Singular*: another, anybody, anyone, anything, each, either, everybody, everyone, everything, little, much, neither, nobody, no one, nothing, one, other, somebody, someone, something) (*Plural*: both, few, many, others, several) (*Either*: all, any, more, most, none, some)
Relative	Connects incomplete thoughts to complete thoughts (that, which, who, whom, whoever, whomever, whichever) *Example*: She is the one <u>who</u> won the prize.
Interrogative	Asks a question *Example*: <u>What</u> will you do? (what, which, who, whom, whose)
Demonstrative	Points out a noun or acts as an adjective *Example*: <u>That</u> is not my dog. (this, that, these, those)
Reflexive	Refers back to the subject (*Singular*: myself, yourself, himself, herself, itself) (*Plural*: ourselves, yourselves, themselves) *Example*: Ella made <u>herself</u> lunch.
Intensive	Emphasizes a noun or pronoun (*Singular*: myself, yourself, himself, herself, itself) (*Plural*: ourselves, yourselves, themselves) *Example*: I bought the tickets <u>myself</u>.

Help Pages

Parts of Speech - Verbs	
Action	Shows an action *Example*: A stunt man <u>performs</u> dangerous feats. The symphony <u>performs</u> every Sunday.
Being	Does not show action; shows a state of being *Examples*: is, are, was, were, be, am, being, been
Linking	Links the subject with a noun or adjective *Examples*: appear, become, feel, seem, smell, taste, sounds, and all forms of *be*
Helping (Auxiliary)	Pairs with a main verb to form a verb phrase *Examples*: is, are, was, were, be, am, being, been, might, could, should, would, can, do, does, did, may, must, will, shall, have, has, had

Verb Tense

Verb tense tells the time when the action or condition of the verb occurs.

Simple Verb Tenses

Present	The action is occurring now or is unchanging.	The house is new. (singular subject) The boys swim. (plural)
Past	The action was started and completed in the past.	The clock stopped. (singular subject) The buses ran. (plural)
Future	The action will not start until the future.	The snow will fall. (singular subject) The lakes will freeze. (plural)

Perfect Verb Tenses

A **perfect verb tense** or **perfect verb form** describes a completed action. All perfect verb forms use past tense verbs with helping verbs.

Present (has / have)	Action is ongoing or indefinite.	Nick <u>has finished</u> two of his assignments. We <u>have played</u> soccer for five years.
Past (had)	Shows which event in the past happened first.	She <u>had asked</u> for help before she began working. The children <u>had napped</u> before coming down to dinner
Future (will have)	Action will occur in the future before some other action.	I <u>will have completed</u> my chores by bedtime. They <u>will have learned</u> the routines by next year.

Progressive Verb Tenses

A main verb that ends in *-ing* works with a helping verb to form the progressive tense. The verb phrase shows action that is ongoing in the present, past, or future.

Present We are talking.	**Past** We were talking.	**Future** We will be talking.

Help Pages

Verb Tense (continued)

Irregular Verbs

Irregular verbs do not follow the patterns of simple or perfect tense. Such verbs must be memorized. Here is a list of some common irregular verbs.

Present	Past	Use with *has, have,* or *had*	Present	Past	Use with *has, have,* or *had*
awake	awoke	awoken	keep	kept	kept
become	became	become	leave	left	left
build	built	built	mistake	mistook	mistaken
catch	caught	caught	ride	rode	ridden
creep	crept	crept	shake	shook	shaken
drink	drank	drunk	shrink	shrank	shrunk
fall	fell	fallen	sneak	sneaked (snuck)	sneaked (snuck)
fight	fought	fought	stink	stank	stunk
forbid	forbade	forbidden	sweep	swept	swept
get	got	gotten	teach	taught	taught
hide	hid	hidden	understand	understood	understood
hear	heard	heard	wind	wound	wound

Parts of Speech - Conjunctions

Conjunctions connect similar words, clauses, or phrases within a sentence.

Coordinating   Join two equal elements or two complete thoughts
                        Use the acronym FANBOYS   (for, and, nor, but, or, yet, so)
                        Example: We swam in the ocean <u>and</u> roasted hot dogs over the fire.

Correlative   Work in pairs to join words
                        either/or   neither/nor   both/and   whether/or   as/as   if/then   not only/but also
                        Example: <u>Neither</u> Jim <u>nor</u> his father cared for mushrooms.

Subordinating   Join a complete thought with an incomplete thought
                        See chart below.
                        Example: Finish your homework <u>before</u> you go outside.

Examples of Subordinating Conjunctions				
after	before	if	though	whenever
although	even if	since	unless	while
as	than	until	wherever	because
how	that	even though	when	till

Help Pages

Parts of Speech - Adverbs

Adverbs That Tell *When*

after	earlier	last	now	seldom	then	when
afterwards	early	late	occasionally	since	today	whenever
again	finally	later	often	sometimes	tomorrow	while
always	first	never	once	soon	until	yesterday
before	frequently	next	permanently	still	usually	yet

Adverbs That Tell *How*

angrily	firmly	happily	noisily	quickly	selfishly	unbelievably
calmly	gracefully	kindly	perfectly	quietly	slowly	wildly
eagerly	greedily	loudly	politely	sadly	softly	willingly

Adverbs That Tell *Where*

away	downstairs	forward	inside	outside	there
back	far	here	near	somewhere	upward

Adverbs That Tell *To What Extent*

almost	completely	permanently	really	too
also	extremely	quite	scarcely	vaguely
barely	more	rather	thoroughly	very

Parts of Speech - Adjectives

Adjectives modify nouns or pronouns. Adjectives tell *how many*, *what color*, *how big*, *how small*, *what kind*, and so on.   **Example**: He was a tall man.

A proper adjective begins with a capital letter.   **Example**: Siberian Husky

An article is a special type of adjective (a, an, the).   **Example**: Throw Jack the ball.

Parts of Speech - Prepositions

Prepositions relate nouns or pronouns to other words in the sentence. A **prepositional phrase** begins with a preposition and ends with a noun or a pronoun.

Some Common Prepositions

about	around	by	into	out	under
above	before	down	near	outside	underneath
across	behind	during	nearby	over	until
after	below	except	next to	past	up
against	beneath	for	of	through	upon
along	beside	from	off	throughout	with
alongside	between	in	on	to	within
among	beyond	inside	onto	toward	without

Parts of Speech – Interjections

An interjection is a word or a phrase that shows emotion (surprise, relief, fear, or anger etc.).
Example: Ouch!   Good grief!   Wow!

Help Pages

Sentences

Parts of a Sentence

Subject	The **simple subject** has no modifier. Every sentence has a simple subject.
	The **complete subject** includes the simple subject plus all of the modifiers that go with it.
	Example: <u>A few ravenous **teenagers**</u> devoured the pizza. *Teenagers* is the simple subject. *A few ravenous teenagers* is the complete subject.
Predicate	The **simple predicate** is the verb.
	The **complete predicate** is the verb plus the other words that say something about the subject – what the subject is or does.
	Example: The tired children **<u>climbed</u>** <u>slowly upstairs</u>. *Climbed* is the simple predicate, or verb. *Climbed slowly upstairs* is the complete predicate.

The Four Sentence Types

Type	Other Name	Punctuation	Example:
declarative	statement	period	This is a sentence.
interrogative	question	question mark	Is this correct?
imperative	command/request	period	Please open the door.
exclamatory	exclamation	exclamation point	This is awesome!

Features of a sentence
1. begins with a capital letter
2. ends with punctuation/end mark
3. conveys a complete thought

Fragments
A fragment is not a sentence because it does not express a complete thought. A fragment is missing either a subject or a verb.

Examples: The book that I read.   (missing a verb)

Running down the street.   (missing a subject)

Run-on Sentences
A run-on is two or more complete thoughts that run together without proper punctuation or conjunctions.

Examples:

Incorrect: Lori wants to be a biologist she likes nature but she does not enjoy being outside if it is cold she is more of a warm weather person some biologists must do research outside so maybe Lori should study something else instead.

Correct: Lori wants to be a biologist because she likes nature. However, Lori does not enjoy being outside if it is cold. She is more of a warm weather person, and some biologists must do research outside. Maybe Lori should study something else instead.

Help Pages

Sentence Structure	
Simple	**Parts:** subject and predicate only **Example:** We will hold a rally at the local park.
Compound	**Parts:** two or more complete thoughts **Joined by:** coordinating conjunction **Example:** There will be speeches in the morning, and we will play games in the afternoon.
Complex	**Parts:** a complete thought and one or more incomplete thoughts **Joined by:** subordinating conjunction **Example:** The rally will last until dusk unless the weather is severe.

Punctuation	
Commas (,)	Use commas to separate words or phrases in a series. ***Example:*** Sun brought a coloring book, some crayons, and a pair of scissors.
	Use a comma to separate two independent clauses joined by a conjunction. ***Example:*** Dad works in the city, and he is a commuter.
	Use a comma to separate two words or two numbers when writing a date. ***Example:*** Friday, April 8, 2011
	Use a comma between the city and state in an address. ***Examples:*** Boston, MA Seattle, WA Honolulu, HI
	Use a comma before or after a quote if there is no end mark. ***Example:*** "You know," said Marta, "Robert is an excellent violinist."
	Place a comma after an introductory word, phrase, or subordinate clause. ***Example:*** Hey, who wants to play tennis? ***Example:*** On the other hand, you may not need any help. ***Example:*** Since it is raining, we will have indoor recess.
	Use a comma to separate the words *yes* and *no* from the rest of a sentence. ***Examples:*** Yes, I will join you. No, thank you.
	Use a comma to separate a "tag question" from the rest of a sentence. ***Examples:*** You saw that, didn't you? George will lead the choir, won't he?
	Use a comma to show direct address. ***Examples:*** Please sit down, Mrs. Schumacher. Come here, Peggy, I want you to meet Mrs. Schumacher.
	Use commas in greetings and closings of letters. ***Examples:*** Dear Mr. Clydesdale, Sincerely yours,
Apostrophe (')	Use an apostrophe to form a contraction or a possessive noun. ***Examples:*** I don't want to go. That was Sherry's little sister.

Help Pages

Punctuation (continued)

Commas and Quotation Marks in Dialogue

Put quotation marks before and after the actual words that someone says. Quotation marks are like a frame around spoken words. Keep the end mark inside the quotes.
Example: She said, "We need to go now."

Do not capitalize words in the middle of a quote unless they are proper nouns or the first word in a sentence.
Example: "That intersection is dangerous!" warned Betsy. "So hold your sister's hand."

Use a comma or end mark before and after a quote.
Examples: "It's starting to rain!" Marcy exclaimed. Mickey replied, "Don't worry, you won't melt."

Do not use a comma at the end of a sentence within quotes if there is another end mark.
Example: "Grandma's here!" exclaimed Sasha.

Capitalization Rules

Capitalize the first word in a sentence, the pronoun *I*, proper nouns, and proper adjectives.

Capitalize the day and the month when writing dates.

Capitalize holidays, product names, and geographic names. These are all proper nouns.

Capitalize the first word and the important words in titles.
Example: *From the Mixed-Up Files of Mrs. Basil E. Frankweiler*

Other Types of Punctuation

Punctuating Titles

Show the title of a book, movie, play, television show, or website by using italics or by underlining it.

Examples:	*Sarah, Plain and Tall*	or	<u>Sarah, Plain and Tall</u>
	Peter and the Wolf	or	<u>Peter and the Wolf</u>
	Sesame Street	or	<u>Sesame Street</u>
	www.Toys.com	or	<u>www. Toys.com</u>

 Put quotation marks around the title of a short work, such as a poem, song, short story, or book chapter.
Examples: "Dreams" is a poem by Langston Hughes.

We sang "Jingle Bells" and many other winter songs.

"The Monkey's Paw" is a scary short story by W.W. Jacobs.

In <u>My Side of the Mountain</u>, by Jean Craighead George, one of the chapters is called "The Old, Old Tree."

Help Pages

Proofreader's Symbols

Description	Symbol	Example
Make capital	≡	the car raced down the street.
Add something	∧	The car raced down street. the
Make lower case	/	The Car raced down the street.
Take something out	℘	The car raced down the the street.
Check spelling	⟨sp⟩	The cor raced down the street.
Indent	¶	¶The car raced down the street.
Add end punctuation	⊙ ⑴ ⑶	The car raced down the street⊙

Greek and Latin Roots and Their Meanings

Root / Meaning		Root / Meaning		Root / Meaning		Root / Meaning	
able	able to	con	with	im, in	not	phobe	fear
agora	open space	de	take away	inter	between	phon	sound
amphi	both	di	two	jus	law	photo	light
ante	before	dia	across	less	without	poly	many
anthropo	human	dict	speak	log/o	word	port	carry
anti	against	dis	not	mal	bad	post	after
astro	star	ex	out of	micro	tiny	pre	before
auto	self	ful	full of	milli	thousand	prim	first
bi	two	geo	earth	mis	bad	pro	for
biblio	book	graph	written	mono	one	re	again
bio	life	gram	written	morph	form	scrib	write
centi	hundred	hemi	half	non	not	script	write
centri	center	hospit	guest	ology	study of	sub	below
chrono	time	hydro	water	pan	all	thermo	heat
circum	around	ible	able	ped	foot	trans	across
co, com	with	il	opposite	philic	fondness	un	not

Help Pages

Figurative Language

A **simile** is a way to describe something using a comparison. A simile compares two things using the words *like* or *as*.

Example: The baby is *as playful as a kitten*. (A baby is compared to a kitten.)

A **metaphor** compares two things but does not use *like* or *as*. It uses a form of the verb *be*.

Example: Joey is *a magnet for bad luck*. (He attracts bad luck.)

Personification gives human features to something non-human.

Example: A battalion of sunflowers stood at attention, facing the commanding officer. (On a farm, sunflowers grow in rows; they are rigid, like soldiers in formation, and the flower always turns toward the sun.)

An **idiom** is a phrase whose meaning can't be understood from the literal meaning of the words.

Example: *This article is way over my head*. This phrase could mean something is taller than me. But when *over my head* is an idiom, it means something is too complicated to be understood.

Examples: We bought a used car, and it's a real lemon!
(refers to a car that has many problems or doesn't run)

At first I was angry, but I got over it.
(refers to letting go of something that was upsetting)

An **adage** or **proverb** is a wise saying that most people think is true. It may give advice.

Example: *All that glitters is not gold*. This saying warns us that something might seem valuable, but it really is not valuable.

Spelling Rules

Adding Prefixes

When adding a prefix or joining two words, do not change the spelling of the base word.

Adding Suffixes that Begin with a Consonant

When adding a suffix that begins with a consonant, do not change the spelling of the base word.

Examples:	joy + ful → joyful	wool + ly → woolly	agree + ment → agreement,
	pain + ful → painful	sincere + ly → sincerely	govern + ment → government
Common Exceptions:	argue + ment → argument	true + ly → truly	nine + th → ninth,
	judge + ment → judgment	due + ly → duly	awe + ful → awful

Adding Suffixes that Begin with a Vowel

When a word ends in a **vowel + y**, add a suffix without changing the spelling of the base word.

Examples: employ + er → employer   play + ing → playing
gray + est → grayest   enjoy + ment → enjoyment

When a word ends in **silent -e**, usually drop the -e to add a suffix that begins with a vowel.

Examples: love + able → lovable

Help Pages

Spelling Rules (continued)

Adding Suffixes that Begin with a Vowel (continued)

When a word ends in a **consonant + y** pattern, usually change the *y* to *i* when adding a suffix.

> ***Examples***: try + ed → tried   (ends in consonant + *y*; change the *y* to *i*)

Do not change the *y* to *i* if the word ends in a vowel + *y* pattern or if the suffix is *ing*.

> ***Examples***: destroy + ed → destroyed   (vowel + *y*)
>
> hurry + ing → hurrying   (consonant + *ing*)

When a one-syllable word ends in the **cvc pattern (consonant - vowel - consonant)**, usually double the final consonant to add a suffix that begins with a vowel.

> ***Examples***: ship + ing → shipping   (suffix begins with a vowel)
>
> ship + ment → shipment   (suffix begins with a consonant)
>
> nut + y → nutty   (suffix is *y*)

When a one-syllable word ends in the **cvc pattern**, and the final consonant is ***s***, ***x*** or ***w***, do not double the final consonant.

> ***Examples***: mix + ing → mixing   box + ed → boxed   slow + er → slower

When a multi-syllable word ends in the **cvc pattern**, and the **accent is on the last syllable**, usually double the final consonant to add a suffix that begins with a vowel.

> ***Example***:   commit + ing → committing   (suffix begins with a vowel)

Common Exception: prefer + able → preferable

Making Plurals

When a word **ends in *s, x, z, ch*, or *sh*** add -*es* to make the plural

> ***Examples***: tax → taxes; wish → wishes

Many words that **end in *f* or *fe***, change the *f* or *fe* to -*ves*.

> ***Examples***: life → lives; thief → thieves

Other words that **end in *f* or *ff*** do not follow the rule for making plurals.

> ***Examples***: cliff → cliffs; belief → beliefs

For words that **end in a consonant + *o***, add an *s* to make the plural.

> ***Examples***: patio → patios

Other words that end in a consonant + *o*, add an *es* to make the plural.

> ***Examples***: tomato → tomatoes

Irregular plural nouns have a completely different spelling in the plural form.

Common irregular plural nouns							
child	children	man	men	ox	oxen	tooth	teeth
louse	lice	mouse	mice	person	people	woman	women

Place *i* before *e*, except after *c*, or when sounded like /ā/ as in neighbor and weigh.

> ***Examples***: mischief   receive   eight

There are many exceptions to spelling rules. If you are not sure of the spelling of a word, use a dictionary to check.

Help Pages

Common Core
ENGLISH GRAMMAR 5
& Mechanics

Answers to Lessons

	Lesson #1		Lesson #2		Lesson #3
1	Example: It was only low on air. (Sentence may vary.)	**1**	B A	**1**	Tanya bakes four kinds of cookies for the PTA bake sale: chocolate chip, oatmeal, peanut butter, and sugar.
2	simple compound	**2**	has written	**2**	nor
3	The plant leaves began to droop since Travis had forgotten to water them again.	**3**	being being action action	**3**	will dress
4	crosses crossed	**4**	either or	**4**	Isabella, did you remember to bring a beach towel? I was certain it was a tie, weren't you? No, thank you.
5	far-fetched	**5**	jordan is a lifeguard this summer at fell lake in northfield, Ohio.	**5**	Creative Kids
6	I loved The Sixty-Eight Rooms, a book about miniature sixth graders.	**6**	spent spends	**6**	thicken
7	The movie that I watched last night...	**7**	preposition adverb	**7**	Proper: Latinos, Chicago, Pizza Hut, Ford Explorer Common: uncle, tourist, automobile, summer
8	Every morning I brush my teeth, pack my backpack, and eat a big breakfast.	**8**	Well, this will be the last time we can bowl here. Hooray, you were the top scorer this round!	**8**	D A E B C
9	its it's	**9**	The fluffy white dog scratched at the back door.	**9**	chef wizard B
10	saturday thanksgiving day january aunt edith ms. martin	**10**	oxen children mice knives	**10**	lice children people teeth

Lesson #4		Lesson #5		Lesson #6	
1	<u>Lila was invited to Ohio's anti-smoking conference</u> because <u>her poster won first place in the county-wide competition</u>.	**1**	They We	**1**	him them us
2	antonyms	**2**	The child whose mittens we found is looking in the lost and found now.	**2**	antonyms
3	B	**3**	but so	**3**	I think it is warm enough to go swimming today, don't you agree?
4	is practicing	**4**	<u>The powerful cougar</u> buries some of its prey to eat later.	**4**	One of the best books i ever read was about a boy who run away from home. He survived in the wilderness for several weeks. ~~No camping gear, food, or cell phone.~~
5	The orchestra is playing well tonight, don't you think?	**5**	B D ? C A !	**5**	for, and, nor, but, or, yet, so
6	Everyone likes Amanda's new bike, but a few of us are too small to ride it.	**6**	outdated	**6**	Henry <u>will have received his diploma by now</u>. Dad <u>was considering taking us to the amusement park</u>.
7	wrote shovels	**7**	C A B	**7**	either or
8	reluctant to talk	**8**	fingers ice C	**8**	B C A
9	will have filled	**9**	is finishing	**9**	<u>icing on the cake</u> B
10	Malika inquired, "Is this the 1500-meter race or the mile run?"	**10**	The <u>time</u> <u>when</u> the team needs to board the bus is noon.	**10**	www.usyouthsoccer.org

	Lesson #7		Lesson #8		Lesson #9
1	their his its **or** his your	**1**	Isabel and <u>I</u> carried our books and returned (them) to the library.	**1**	Ben and Ella rewarded (themselves) by jogging the last lap. We studied (ourselves) in the mirror.
2	for or	**2**	Mom and Dad traveled <u>throughout the Midwest</u>. Mom bought a magnet <u>from</u> <u>every state</u>. I put them all <u>on</u> <u>our</u> <u>refrigerator</u>.	**2**	Example: The storm caused a power outage, but that won't spoil our fun. (Sentence may vary.)
3	Although it was freezing cold, the family bundled up and went for a walk.	**3**	whether or	**3**	I washed the glasses and put them <u>in the</u> <u>cupboard</u>.
4	Lexie answered, "I got my nickname from my little brother."	**4**	I am taking English, American History, French, and gym this semester. I would adopt an older dog from the shelter, wouldn't you?	**4**	will have sprouted
5	We wore our Halloween costumes and trick-or-treated <u>at</u> every house <u>with</u> a lighted front door <u>on</u> our street.	**5**	had advised had grown had hiked	**5**	antonyms
6	C C	**6**	<u>will wash</u> future <u>scrubs</u> present <u>fed</u> past	**6**	B . C . D ! A ?
7	B C A	**7**	is practicing am waiting	**7**	A C B
8	when	**8**	covers	**8**	A
9	stupidly playfully lightly elegantly	**9**	<u>Despicable Me 2</u> <u>Despicable Me</u>	**9**	Theresa lifesaver
10	The brown bear awoke <u>groggily</u>, but it was fishing <u>hungrily</u> in no time.	**10**	I practiced diving off the high board all summer, and I am getting very good.	**10**	... <u>costs an arm and a leg</u>. Example: very expensive (Meanings may vary.)

Lesson #10		Lesson #11		Lesson #12	
1	(Most) plural (Most) singular	**1**	loaves ____ are dough ____ is	**1**	C
2	If then	**2**	Florida is a peninsula, and its name means "full of flowers."	**2**	C A B
3	If the sun comes out, we will spend the day snorkeling.	**3**	Levi ate his lunch <u>under the tree</u> <u>between two houses</u>.	**3**	✓ *Indigenous* is an adjective.
4	who whose	**4**	have walked has walked	**4**	Patrick and i wrote about the many (noticable)sp (improvments)sp that were made on the hiking trail this Fall⊙
5	bossiness cried merriment	**5**	B C A	**5**	<u>Shade-loving flowers</u> (grow) nicely near the tree line.
6	obeyed enjoyable keyless	**6**	✓ Lewis and Clark... study its plants and animals.	**6**	their there They're
7	solemn	**7**	<u>Because of Winn-Dixie</u>	**7**	(musician) <u>who</u>
8	I see my orthodontist, <u>dr.</u> <u>trents</u>, on <u>saturdays</u>, and we get ice cream at <u>handel's</u> afterwards. Dr. Trents Saturdays Handel's	**8**	scent	**8**	or then
9	synonyms	**9**	<u>Four juicy peaches were</u> <u>hanging on a branch just</u> <u>out of our reach</u>. peaches were hanging	**9**	manageable management enforceable enforcement containable containment
10	C B A	**10**	except because	**10**	ball arrow

	Lesson #13		Lesson #14		Lesson #15
1	<u>socks</u> are <u>money</u> is	**1**	A C B	**1**	is are
2	puzzle	**2**	tenacious	**2**	clear
3	...is traveling <u>tomorrow</u> to see her.	**3**	to two too	**3**	My favorite activities at camp are kayaking, painting, kickball, and swimming.
4	adjective (mī **noot**) noun (**mĭn** ĭt)	**4**	catches	**4**	The first site <u>that</u> we chose...
5	...<u>he needs to earn money to repair his bicycle</u>.	**5**	will be driving will be stopping	**5**	Yes, Phillip and I... ... camping skill, don't you agree?
6	Wow, she baked cookies, muffins, cupcakes, and brownies for the team picnic!	**6**	who	**6**	Marcus couldn't find his way around his new town, so <u>he made himself a map of his important destinations.</u>
7	5 2 1 4 3	**7**	<u>not only</u> <u>but also</u> <u>If</u> <u>then</u> <u>Neither</u> <u>nor</u>	**7**	<u>hit the books</u> ✓ study
8	hydrosphere fear of water hydrophobia water-powered electricity production hydroelectric water layer on earth	**8**	C A B	**8**	~~Camping, hiking, orienteering, and more.~~ Example: He looked forward to camping, hiking, orienteering, and more. (Sentence will vary.)
9	~~potatos~~ ~~reciept~~ neighbor ~~happyness~~ potatoes receipt happiness	**9**	quickly slowly	**9**	marcus put the library and the swiming pool on his map. He labeled it springfield, ohio and dated it september 15, 2015. Marcus, library, swimming, Springfield, Ohio, September
10	<u>has walked</u> present perfect	**10**	<u>The tiny stray kitten</u> <u>lapped up all the milk in the bowl.</u> kitten lapped	**10**	Wait, Help!

	Lesson #16		Lesson #17		Lesson #18
1	was	**1**	Brian and his <s>M</s>om sailed over the <u>a</u>egean <u>s</u>ea to <u>i</u>stanbul, the capital of <u>t</u>urkey.	**1**	synonyms
2	B C A	**2**	E E	**2**	fell falling fallen
3	agreeable	**3**	<u>is packing</u> present <u>will be spending</u> future	**3**	C A B
4	will have fixed have sung had sung had forgotton will have forgotton	**4**	synonyms	**4**	✓ means "understood without being stated" ✓ is an adjective
5	"The Frog Prince" is one of the short stories we were assigned from the book <u>A Treasury of Fairy Tales</u>.	**5**	<u>The rescue helicopter lifted the victims out of the choppy waters</u>.	**5**	<u>to think outside the box</u> ✓ approach the problem in new and novel ways
6	<s>walked</s> walks	**6**	B A C	**6**	The book <u>that</u> Miss Hunt...
7	then but also	**7**	I need balloons, candles, a piñata, and crepe paper. ... fit in the piñata, don't you think?	**7**	its their theirs ours
8	were extinguishing	**8**	<u>rock the boat</u> ✓ disrupt a satisfactory situation	**8**	... by the governor of our state, the mayor of our town, and several news crews.
9	C A B D	**9**	had slept have slept will have slept	**9**	<u>whether</u> <u>or</u> <u>not only</u> but also
10	pre- after inter- between post- before	**10**	We wanted to take the bus into town, but the bus was already full.	**10**	<u>Coolmath4kids</u>

	Lesson #19		Lesson #20		Lesson #21
1	is are	**1**	C <u>would go</u> A <u>would prefer</u> B <u>would..: be</u>	**1**	(Knights) <u>defended</u> (They) <u>were</u>
2	(can) ^Mgo	**2**	Example: The fireworks exploded in a burst of color over our back yard. (Sentences will vary.)	**2**	<u>student</u> whom
3	are skiing is visiting	**3**	<u>I ordered an extra-large ice cream cone,</u> (but) <u>most of it dripped down my arm.</u>	**3**	
4	~~Rubber band and friendship bracelets.~~ verb	**4**	froze blew	**4**	SIZE (gigantic tiny immense) SHAPE (circular square triangular round) OPINION (silly kind tasty happy likeable lazy) AGE (younger ancient elderly)
5	well adverb	**5**	C B A	**5**	NUMBER (dozen single two five) COLOR (pink turquoise purple black)
6	as / as	**6**	persevere	**6**	will be studying
7	"That's a great idea, and we'll have time if we get started now," added Henrique.	**7**	<u>Everyone in the back row</u> <u>screamed at the same moment.</u>	**7**	B A
8	B A C	**8**	(driver) <u>whose</u>	**8**	Roberto won two gold medals in swimming, but he did not break a world record.
9	delicate pink scratchy green	**9**	...<u>over the</u> (horizon).	**9**	<u>throughout</u> the (year) <u>above</u> the deep blue (sea) <u>around</u> the last sharp (bend)
10	We're going to ... <u>tomorrow</u>.	**10**	~~open~~ opened	**10**	<u>I brought you a gift</u> (since) <u>your birthday is next month.</u>

	Lesson #22		Lesson #23		Lesson #24
1	D A C B	**1**	few, somebody, everyone, many that, who, which our, my	**1**	B A
2	<u>ungrateful</u>　<u>delicious</u>	**2**	is changing	**2**	A B
3	<u>Sabrina popped a big bowl of popcorn</u> (before) <u>we sat down to watch the movie</u>.	**3**	A B	**3**	B
4	orb	**4**	glittery round	**4**	C
5	<u>knowledgeable</u>　<u>proficient</u> <u>educated</u>	**5**	<u>actors</u>　who	**5**	(along) <u>streets</u> (through) <u>fields</u>　(into) <u>river</u>
6	Wow! It is almost midnight.	**6**	~~Pistachio, cheese strudel, hazelnut, and bubble gum.~~ Example: Some of my favorites are pistachio, cheese strudel, hazelnut, and bubble gum. (Sentence will vary.)	**6**	have won
7	preposition adverb	**7**	✓ *Gaunt* rhymes with *haunt*. ✓ The opposite of *gaunt* is *plump*.	**7**	is washing
8	was voting were going	**8**	<u>What</u>　<u>where</u>	**8**	✓ Sheila knocks on the door and walked in.
9	<u>Candy Crush</u> <u>Bud, Not Buddy</u> "Friendzzzzz"	**9**	<u>around the bend</u>	**9**	or
10	<u>stole my thunder</u> She revealed my good news before I could. (Meanings may vary.)	**10**	effect	**10**	Violet tossed greens, carrots, broccoli, celery, and pears in a salad fit for a king.

	Lesson #25		Lesson #26		Lesson #27
1	<u>dog</u> that	**1**	(book) that	**1**	A B
2	B C D A	**2**	were pounding	**2**	crunchy old delicate new
3	Example: The students will also take a cruise and go to Notre Dame. (Sentence will vary.)	**3**	B A	**3**	(Leonardo Da Vinci, a great inventor) <u>designed a submarine and a</u> <u>helicopter in the 1400s.</u>
4	rays raise	**4**	greedily, mysteriously, lazily muggy, shady, hungry	**4**	board bored
5	have mistaken	**5**	<u>E.T. the Extra-Terrestrial</u>	**5**	... <u>she fell on the playground.</u> <u>To celebrate Tim's birthday</u>...
6	will have played	**6**	B	**6**	My favorite Amusement park it is cedar point in ohio because it has the best roller coasters⊙
7	arrangement fanciful lovable loyally	**7**	had eaten had prepared	**7**	postpone pretest antifreeze
8	Farmer Jean composts leftover corn, lettuce, carrots, and tomatoes.	**8**	children people geese oxen	**8**	pronoun adjective adjective
9	Dr. Fisher is my dentist, and Dr. Richards is my orthodontist. (Sentence may vary.)	**9**	✓ Last winter there were many bluejays in our back yard, and we took their picture every day.	**9**	B C
10	"Let's walk to the skateboard park," suggested Erica. "We can get an ice cream cone on the way home," she added.	**10**	I couldn't eat another bite, could you? Yes, I would love to go again.	**10**	<u>on the house</u> Example: It was free. (Meanings will vary.)

Lesson #28		Lesson #29		Lesson #30	
1	(Since) Ricky was almost sixteen, he began to take driving lessons.	**1**	four shiny miniature	**1**	is practicing are practicing
2	sailors　who	**2**	through threw coarse course	**2**	dozen tiny brown
3	chewy rectangular twenty-four oval	**3**	have borrowed	**3**	adverb
4	B C A	**4**	preposition adverb	**4**	A dragon slayer! verb
5	exhausted energized	**5**	(singer) whose	**5**	took firm action
6	"I haven't called Marissa, Hannah, or Louisa since I lost my phone," Henry explained.	**6**	is the pizza ~~which~~ ^that you ordered arriving before noon⑦	**6**	C B A
7	not only　/　but also	**7**	simile Example: glowing (Synonyms may vary.)	**7**	a machine on skates metaphor
8	✓ Of course, Skip is the best goalie, don't you think?	**8**	will be driving will be testing	**8**	Today　faster
9	departure	**9**	My favorite holidays are Thanksgiving Day, Valentine's Day, and Halloween.	**9**	friends who dog that
10	(see table below)	**10**	New Kid on the Block "I Wonder Why Dad is So Thoroughly Mad."	**10**	In spite of being warned, I forgot my homework again. Yes, I think Steve did pick up the recycling, didn't he?

Lesson #28, item 10:

	Part of Speech	Meaning
ingenious	adjective	very smart
persevere	verb	stick with a task
enigma	noun	a mystery

(Wording will vary.)